Ready to Read
Animal Adventures

How to Play

1. Press the Power button to turn the SD-X Reader on or off. The LED will light up when the SD-X Reader is on.

2. Touch the volume buttons found on this page to adjust the volume.

3. Touch words and pictures on the page to hear audio. These icons start the following activities:

🔲	Hear the Page	🔍	Find It
📢	Hear the Word	📖	Word Play
🔤	Spell the Word	🎵	Hear the Music
🔊	Sound Out the Word	💿	Sing Along

4. Find the monkey on each spread and touch him with the SD-X Reader.

5. After two minutes of inactivity, the SD-X Reader will beep and go to sleep.

6. If the batteries are low, the SD-X Reader will beep twice and the LED will start blinking. Replace the batteries by following the instructions on the preceding page. The SD-X Reader uses two AAA batteries.

7. To use headphones or earbuds, plug them into the headphone jack on the SD-X Reader.

Volume

 Publications International, Ltd.

Pinky Digs a Hole

Many pigs play in the puddle.

The pigs bump Pinky. They push her.
They step on her. There is no room for
Pinky. She wants her own puddle.

Pinky says to the pigs: I do not want to
share a puddle.

Pinky makes a new puddle.

She finds a spot by the river. She digs a hole. Then she fills the hole with water.

Pinky says: My very own puddle!

Pinky likes her puddle.

Pinky plays in her puddle.

She splashes mud. No one splashes her back.

She splashes again. No one splashes her back.

Pinky looks at the other puddle.
The pigs splash each other. They
roll around. They laugh.

Pinky is sad. She is alone in her puddle.

Pinky says: I miss my friends.

Pinky calls to the pigs: Look at my puddle.

The pigs go to her puddle.

The pigs say: Great puddle!

Pinky splashes the pigs with mud.
They splash her back. Pinky laughs.

Pinky says: Sharing is fun.

Timmy and His Stripes

Timmy looks at himself in the water.
He sees stripes.

Timmy says to Dad: I do not like stripes.
What can I do?

Dad says: All tigers have stripes. I
like your stripes.

Timmy shakes his head. He
walks away.

Timmy sees a patch of flowers. The flowers are red.

Timmy picks the flowers. He covers his stripes with the flowers.

Timmy smiles. He says: No more stripes.

Then the wind blows. The flowers fly away. Timmy sees his stripes again.

Timmy walks to a mud puddle. He rolls in the mud. The mud covers Timmy.

Timmy smiles. He says: No more stripes.

Then Dad comes to the puddle. Dad says: You are dirty. You need a bath.

Dad washes Timmy. Timmy sees his stripes again.

Dad says to Timmy: We will play a game. Close your eyes. Then find me when I call.

Timmy closes his eyes. He waits for Dad to call.

Dad calls: Find me.

Timmy looks around. He does not find Dad.

Timmy looks some more. He does not find Dad.

Dad stands up. He says: Here I am.
Dad is right next to Timmy.

Dad says: Stripes look like grass. Tigers hide
in the grass. Stripes are good.

Timmy likes that idea.

He runs off to play hide-and-seek
with his friends.

All the Pretty Little Horses

Hush-a-bye, don't you cry.
Go to sleep, little baby.
And when you wake, you shall have a cake,
And all the pretty little horses.

Little brown ones, little red ones,
All the pretty little horses.
All the blue ones, all the pink ones,
All the pretty little horses.

Hush-a-bye, don't you cry.
Go to sleep, little baby.
And when you wake, you shall have a cake,
And all the pretty little horses.

Little blue ones, little green ones,
All the pretty little horses.
All the white ones, all the black ones,
All the pretty little horses.

Mary Had a Little Lamb

Mary had a little lamb,
little lamb, little lamb.
Mary had a little lamb, its
fleece was white as snow.

Everywhere that Mary went,
Mary went, Mary went,
Everywhere that Mary went,
the lamb was sure to go.

B-I-N-G-O

There was a farmer had a dog,
And Bingo was his name-o.
B-I-N-G-O!
B-I-N-G-O!
B-I-N-G-O!
And Bingo was his name-o!